W9-CRW-780

Penguin Handbooks

VOGUE GUIDE TO MAKE-UP

Felicity Clark has been Beauty Editor of *Vogue* since 1972. She started her career in public relations and later worked for five years in New York as executive assistant to Diana Vreeland, then Editor-in-chief of American *Vogue*. She joined Condé Nast in London in 1969.

As the daughter of a regular army officer, she travelled a lot as a child – and has continued doing so in her job. She is an active sportswoman and a gifted musician – she played the flute in the National Youth Orchestra.

She has worked with leading photographers all over the world. Lord Snowdon says: 'She is one of the most professional editors that I have ever worked with. There are many assignments that I would not have been able to do without her tremendous contribution. It is the back-up that she supplies, the amount of research and meticulous attention to detail that she puts in beforehand. On the assignment itself, she manages to create an atmosphere that stimulates and encourages everyone involved.'

VOGUE GUIDE TO MAKE-UP

FELICITY CLARK

PENGUIN BOOKS

Penguin Books Ltd, Harmondsworth, Middlesex, England
Penguin Books, 625 Madison Avenue, New York, New York 10022, U.S.A.
Penguin Books Australia Ltd, Ringwood, Victoria, Australia
Penguin Books Canada Ltd, 2801 John Street, Markham, Ontario, Canada L3R 1B4
Penguin Books (N.Z.) Ltd, 182–190 Wairau Road, Auckland 10, New Zealand

First published 1981

Made and printed in Great Britain by Butler & Tanner Ltd, Frome and London

Set in Monophoto Photina
Composition by Filmtype Services Limited, Scarborough, England

The pictures of Queen Henrietta Maria, Catherine of Braganza
and Queen Alexandra on pages 8 and 9 are reproduced by courtesy
of the National Portrait Gallery, London.

Designed by Patrick Yapp

Contents

Introduction   7

Make-up Routine   13

An A-Z of Equipment and Products   30

The Right Light: What a Difference It Makes   37

The Weather: How It Affects Your Looks   41

Expert Make-up for Different Skin Colourings   47

Expert Make-up for the Woman over Thirty-five   53

Colour Co-ordination: What to Wear with What   58

Your Face: How to Change Its Shape   61

Changing the Shape of Your Face   62

Hands and Feet: How to Add the Final Touch   73

Scent: How to Make the Most of Its Fragrant Aura   79
   An A-Z of Perfumes and Ingredients   81

Index   89

Introduction

It's incredible to think that for about 6,000 years women – and men – have used cosmetics. And, although the art of make-up has come quite a long way since early Egyptian ladies painted their faces, anointed their bodies and spent so many hours achieving the dramatic effects we associate with legendary beauties like Queen Nefertiti and Cleopatra, the amazing thing is that the basic cosmetic items remain the same. For hair: shampoos, conditioners and colourants; for face: foundation, eyeshadow, kohl, cheek rouge, lip and nail colour from the herb henna; for skin: creams and oil for both face and body; and, of course, perfume. They may have been crude in content, colour and texture, and there was obviously not nearly so much choice, but the categories were the same.

The Chinese are thought to have been the first to experiment with make-up, then the Egyptians who probably learned about the art from travellers returning from China and who have left us much more positive evidence, owing to their habit of burying personal possessions with mummified bodies in tombs. The excavation of these tombs has enabled museums today to display ancient relics of once vital beauty routines: cosmetic pots, which still contained traces of ointments when discovered; toilet spoons; containers for kohl, and sticks for its application; palettes, bowls and pestles for grinding and mixing cosmetic colours; polished metal mirrors; and, of course, the valuable perfume containers. Also, there were hair-care aids – combs, curling tongs, etc. And many of these beautiful objects were fashioned from rare woods, ivory, alabaster and so on, in the shape of animals, birds and

Greek fresco, Minoan 1500 BC, Catherine de' Medici, Queen Henrietta Maria

insects. This proves the high esteem in which cosmetics were held, the priceless value of perfume and the passion for beauty that obsessed women in those early times.

The desire to paint face and body is one of the most primitive known to man, appearing throughout the ancient civilizations. The art can be traced through the Chinese, Japanese, Indians, South Sea Islanders, Maoris, Aborigines, Africans, South and North American Indians. All used face and body decorations in their traditional and ceremonial cultures and still do. Hands and feet tattooed with henna are still to be found in Morocco and other North African countries.

Many centuries before Christ the Sumerians, Assyrians, Persians and Phoenicians were among those who set enormous store by scent, cosmetics and decorative substances. Early Christian men and women devoted long hours to their toilets – despite the fury of religious leaders who preached strongly against all forms of vanity. And bathing and beautifying were early developed by the Indian people into religious rituals which still exist.

The Greeks were slower to accept painted faces – but they were eventually responsible for popularizing whitened complexions, achieved, unfortunately, through the use of white lead (later called ceruse), which proceeded to ruin women's complexions through all the whims of fashion for centuries. Compounds of lead were still in use as recently as the end of the 19th century. More favourably, the Greeks are sometimes credited with the invention of scent – in their mythology, Aphrodite is said to have been the brilliant innovator. In these early times, the popularity of scent varied with the seasons – musk in winter, camphor in summer, for instance –

Catherine of Braganza, Sarah Bernhardt, Queen Alexandra

and, quite apart from various scented products including incense and the cosmetic colours and creams that were available, baths were considered important enough for the production of scented, softening, water-additives. For centuries it was the heads of state, their consorts and the ladies and gentlemen who surrounded them who influenced fashions in hair, make-up and dress. Legendary beauties like Helen of Troy and the Queen of Sheba paved the way for Nero's Empress Poppaea, Catherine de' Medici, Lucretia Borgia, the Saxon Queen Matilda and Eleanor of Aquitaine, who all showed an intense interest in their appearance. Elizabeth I was fascinated by fashion news from abroad, wore scented gloves, bathed in scented waters and employed her ladies in the still-room making herbal lotions and potions for beautifying purposes.

Royal marriages – such as Charles I's to the French Henrietta Maria, Charles II's to the Portuguese Catherine of Braganza and George IV's to Caroline of Brunswick – linked countries throughout Europe and this helped spread new ideas. In this way, new styles emerged from the influence of, for instance, the exotic beauty of Napoleon's Joséphine, born in Martinique, or the cool looks of German Alexandra who married the last Czar of Russia.

In 19th-century England dandies like Beau Brummell outshone the ladies, and aristocratic female beauty dimmed into an era of Victorian disapproval, insipid and plain. Focus began to transfer itself from royal and high-society beauties to stage personalities – like Lola Montez, Lillie Langtry and Sarah Bernhardt – widening in the 20th century to include cinema and television stars.

Interest in the beauty of royalty was revived by King Edward's Queen Alexandra, who when she was Princess of Wales led the

9

Consuelo Vanderbilt, Marlene Dietrich, Sophia Loren

fashion for painted faces; American beauties like Consuelo Vanderbilt and Jennie Jerome captured public imagination with their
wealth, beauty and marriages to the Duke of Marlborough and
Lord Randolph Churchill; the Gibson girls still epitomize a certain
type of beauty. Then came the 1914–18 war, after which nothing
was the same. The emancipation of women brought many changes
in appearance – women cut their hair, showed their ankles and
expressed an individualism in their looks. The wide distribution of
silent movies with stars like Theda Bara and Marion Davies created
a demand for cosmetics, to help women achieve the same sort of
looks, and a mass interest in beauty that is still growing today. In
the thirties, films developed sound, and it was actresses like Marlene Dietrich and Greta Garbo who became idolized for their looks
and as influential as society figures.

The Second World War, however, brought an economy in
fashion – simple to manage, neat, practical hair styles, powder,
lipstick, square shoulders and short skirts were the style of the
forties, relieved by dreams of looking like the screen goddesses of
the time – Betty Grable, Bette Davis and Hedy Lamarr, for instance.
The lean years after the war were filled with bright new faces
starring in serious but glamorized war stories – Margaret Lock-
wood, Deborah Kerr, Ava Gardner – to be followed by the magic
of Marilyn Monroe, Sophia Loren and Audrey Hepburn and then
by the emergence of the fashion model as an influence in the fifties.

Since the end of the war the beauty business has boomed.
Modern products are of a quality vastly superior to those of 6,000
years ago, choice is limitless, and their application has progressed

Elizabeth Taylor, Fiona Campbell-Walter, Twiggy

to a very fine art indeed. However, it is still interesting to note that many recent make-up fashions are simply re-creations of age-old ideas. Heavily black-lined Cleopatra eyes were made popular in the forties when Vivien Leigh played the part, and again, a few years later, when Elizabeth Taylor starred in the re-make of the film; the whitened complexions and huge eyes of the late sixties were reminiscent of those ashen-faced ladies who died of lead poisoning. And, in the seventies, it was fashionable for a time, as in the Middle Ages, to completely pluck out eyebrows.

In England the fifties fashion-page images of Barbara Goalen, Fiona Campbell-Walter and Anne Gunning gave way to the swinging sixties of Jean Shrimpton and the talents of Vidal Sassoon and Mary Quant; Twiggy took her looks into the seventies. Then, the scene shifted across the Atlantic and fashion encouraged a healthy, girl-next-door kind of naturalness, which needed a lot of make-up expertise if it was not to fall into the trap of looking pale and uninteresting. The alternative was sharply contrasting: with bright, glittering make-up for disco dancing and disco lighting.

Make-up should be fun, it should make you look and feel better – and younger, if necessary. Even if a new idea seems to have been used somewhere before, there is always a fresh twist with a new colour or a new fashion face to inspire you; this book aims to bring you up-to-date – to show you how to understand make-up, how to apply it and how to look right *now*.

There are two companion books to this one – *Vogue Guide to Skin Care* and *Vogue Guide to Hair Care*, also published by Penguin.

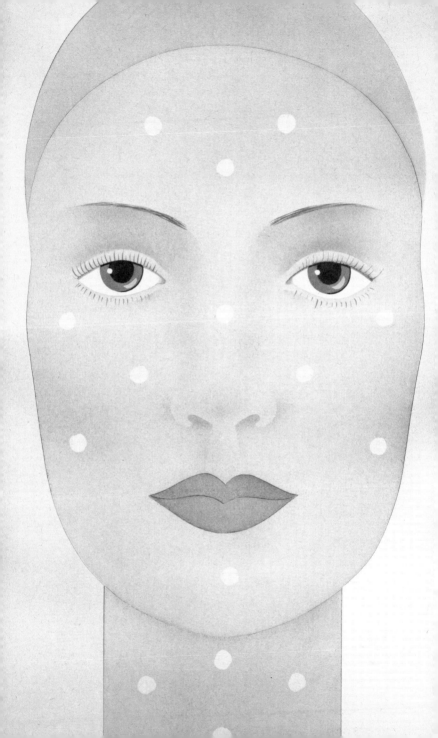

Make-up Routine

Stage One: Cleanse, Tone, Moisturize

Before starting to apply your make-up, you must give yourself the best possible base to work on. This means skin in good condition – which comes from the correct, regular skin-care regime for your skin type, a well-balanced diet (including lots of mineral water), enough sleep, and enough exercise to rev up your circulation. All these ingredients contribute to the appearance of your skin – its clarity, tone and texture. Every time you start to make up, check first that your skin is scrupulously clean. What you cleanse with depends on your skin type and your personal preference for a lotion, cream, foam or soap-and-water. Having cleansed, wipe away any last traces of dirt, debris or grease with a skin freshener or toner – again, which you use depends on your skin type: non-alcoholic fresheners are for dry and sensitive skins, those with alcohol (usually called astringents) are only for oily skins. People with combination skins (patches of dry skin or a t-shape of greasiness down the centre of the face) are wise to use both, or a toner with only a tiny amount of alcohol, diluted (by soaking a cotton-wool pad in water first) for the dry patches.

Cleanse and Tone

Use cool water or non-alcoholic skin tonic.

Moisturize

Dot all over face and neck and blend gently. Don't use too much. Excess moisturizer will only evaporate on the skin and make it drier.

The last step in preparation is moisturizing. Moisturizers are probably the biggest breakthrough in skin care in recent years – they provide a film over the skin that prevents its natural moisture from escaping and causing dehydration, which is the main cause of wrinkles and skin ageing. They also protect the skin from environmental damage – from wind, cold, sun (providing they contain a sunscreen), pollution – especially when no foundation is worn, and help enormously in the smooth application of foundation, as they leave the skin in a soft, supple condition.

Tinted moisturizers are very helpful under foundation to help balance out skin tones. A green tint will tone down redness; mauve reduces sallowness; apricot will warm up a washed-out pallor. But, don't use too much or the result will veer towards the opposite extreme.

Stage Two: Foundation and Camouflage
Foundation, or base, should be considered as a skin improver, something that will give the impression of better, smooth and even-

Dark Circles under the Eyes
Find the dark patches by lowering your head and looking up into a mirror. Gently dot concealer sparingly on the circle and blend by patting with the fingertip. Don't rub or drag. If circle is accompanied by a 'bag' don't let the concealer go over it – this only accentuates it. Powder very lightly if necessary – but avoid powdering under the eyes if possible as it sinks in and deepens tiny lines.

Foundation
Choose to match your skin tone. Apply with damp sponge or fingers. Be careful to blend around nose and chin and fade away under chin. Don't take it into hair line, nor heavily under eyes – it can make tiny lines look deeper than they are.

Eric Boman

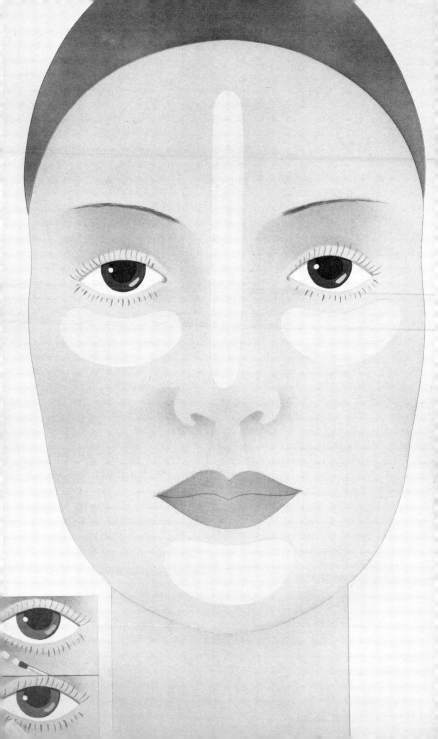

toned skin, while the product itself is almost invisible. Heavy foundation is old-fashioned and ageing; it should never appear mask-like or obvious. Contemporary foundations are light and should be applied sparingly and blended in well. The shade chosen should be as close to your natural skin tone as possible, so that there is no sudden change of colour between chin and neck. This way the end result should be an all-over quality of tone and texture, with just a transparent glaze. Never select your foundation shade by trying it on the back of the hand – the skin here is almost always a totally different colour from that on your face. Test them on the side of your cheek, just above the jawbone, and make your decision in a good light.

Only the very young, or those lucky enough to have near-perfect skin, can really get away with wearing no foundation at all if they want to look their best. But, many people have good skin and only need help in certain areas – chin, forehead or nose, for instance – and can just use the foundation to improve tone in patches, blending it into the surrounding skin for an even effect. In summer, or for sports, a bronze gel is often sufficient, providing just a healthy overall glow.

Foundations are available in various forms – liquids, gels, creams, cream-foams, or solid creams in sticks, blocks or cakes. Which you choose is a matter of how much clarity or cover you want – and personal preference. Most of them are water-in-oil emulsions, with some oil-free liquid formulas especially for oily skins; the all-in-one mixtures of cream and powder which give a very matt finish are best for oily skins too. They should be applied by dotting over the central area of the face, then blending outwards with a damp (not wet) sponge and finishing off with the tips of your fingers; pay particular attention around the hairline and jaw-line that there is no sudden change of tone – and around nostrils, nose and lips. A bit of camouflage is often necessary to cover up the odd spot, patch of discolouration under eyes, scar or other blemish. A heavy cream foundation is suitable, in the same tone as your normal one but in a much lighter shade; also, there are special concealers in sticks or thick cream formulas available, sometimes with their own sponge applicators, which are easy to use. Dot the concealer on the required area, then pat or lightly press it in – use a small amount to start with; you can always add more – then blend the outer edges carefully into the surrounding skin. The technique for covering blemishes is the same whether you are wearing foundation or just moisturizer.

Stage Three: Shape, Blush, Powder
Blusher has taken over the role of old-fashioned rouge. Before there was rouge, or before it was considered permissible to wear it, women used to pinch their cheeks to bring up the colour, knowing it was the best natural way of making the most of their looks. Now, blusher is probably the single most flattering piece of make-up you can possess. It comes in cream, gel or powder form and is the next step in your make-up routine if you choose the cream variety, which includes pencils; if you choose powder blusher, it should be applied after face powder; if you choose the gel variety it is applied over foundation, and face powder shouldn't be used at all – it is designed for the most transparent effect and so would serve no purpose.

Whichever variety you choose, how it is placed on the cheek is vital. The trick is to stare straight ahead of you into a mirror and put a finger directly below your eyeball on your cheekbone. The blusher should be placed there and then blended along the cheekbone towards the hairline. Be careful not to take it too close to your nose, eye or the hollow of your cheek. It's meant to make you look healthy, not feverish. Nobody's face is perfect and bad contouring or shaping can easily end up looking like dirty marks or a heavy bruise. So, if you want to hollow your cheeks, slim your nose or reduce your jaw-line, use the minimum of colour and the lightest touch. Choose a darker shade of foundation or blusher, avoid red tones and test the effects on a friend – to make sure you haven't

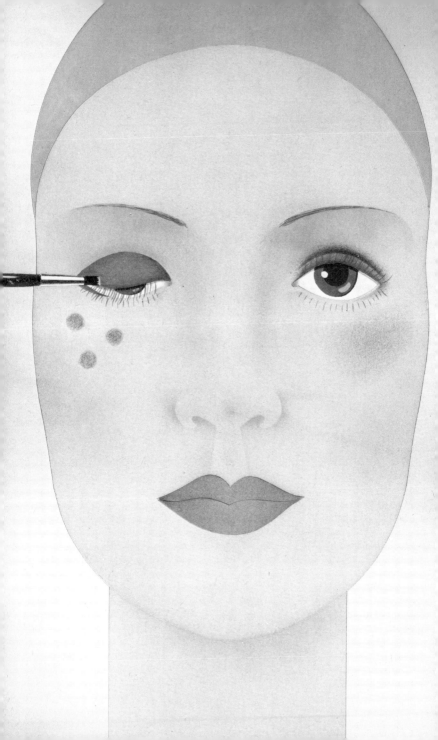

made matters worse. It's often better to play up your good points and forget what you consider the bad ones – they're never so obvious to other people.

As far as blusher colour is concerned, either pinch your cheeks and choose the shade nearest this natural blush or pick one similar in colour to the clothes you wear next to your face. For instance, with wine, crimson or purple clothes, try deep to medium true pink; with orangey shades, peach or tawny tones work best; and with beiges or tans, try the tawny corals or russets. Anything that is pearlized or has gold or silver in it should be left for evening make-up – and they are particularly effective with a tan.

If you want your make-up to last through the day or evening without requiring much repair, face powder is an essential part of the routine. Keep loose powder on your dressing table and carry a compact of pressed powder around with you. Translucent powders are the most popular now – used not to add any colour but to set make-up. They should be used after any cream product you are applying (blusher or cream eye colour; if used after the first coat of lipstick has been applied and blotted, they help stop 'bleeding'

Cream Eye Shadow
Apply after the foundation, before the powder. Use a brush and blend with a clean brush or fingertips, all over lid or wherever it suits you. Fade away at the edges and put a little under the eye if you like, use translucent powder when you powder your face.

Cream Blusher
Put on the cheek bone. Find the correct place by squeezing your index finger on the outer edge of the bone under your eye, your thumb beneath; it should make an 'egg' shape, the wide bit nearer to the outside edges of the face. Blend well, not too far in towards the nose. Left half of the face shows the action, right half the effect.

around the lips) but before any powder colour. A good trick is to dust over much more powder than necessary and then brush off the excess – this ensures its lasting effect. Check that there are no dusty patches and that it is well blended around the nostrils and below the lips.

Stage Four: Eyes

Your eyes are one of your most unique features, and they're one of the most sensitive too. They instantly reflect emotions, respond to wind, dust, glare, lack of sleep, a smoky atmosphere, alcohol and over-indulgence, ill-health and even your sleeping position. It's a good idea to protect them from wind, dust and glare with sunglasses, to keep the delicate skin around the eye area well moisturized with a special eye cream, to remove eye make-up with special eye make-up remover, and to try not to get into the habit of sleeping with your eyes scrunched into the pillow, as this can encourage lines. A healthy diet, lots of mineral water, plenty of sleep and exercise all help to keep your eyes bright and sparkling.

Treating your eyes with care is an investment and ensures they look their best. Furthermore, the eye area provides infinite scope

Powder Blusher

Apply this the same way as cream blusher but with a brush after powdering your face. Right side of face shows the action, left side the effect.

Powder Eye Shadow

After powdering the face apply eye shadow with applicator or brush, all over lids, in the socket, on the browbone, under lower lid, wherever it suits you best. Apply lightly, blend carefully at the edges – make sure it goes all the way into your lashes. Be sparing, powder shadows can make the skin look crepey if too heavily applied.

Eric Boman

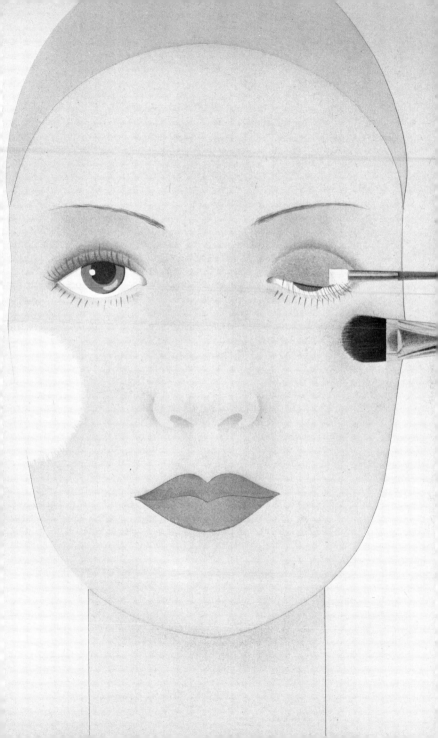

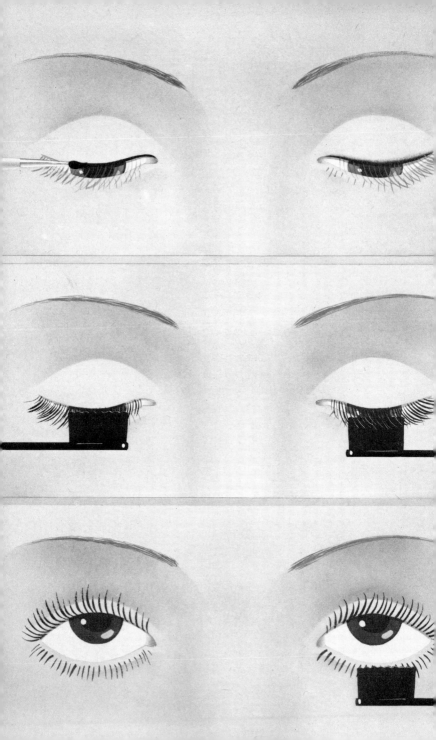

for the most imaginative make-up. It can be just a question of enhancing the eyes naturally with neutral shadows and mascara or really going to town with colour and shape. Whichever it is to be, your eyes are where contact is normally made with another person, the feature they see first; it is important to know how to use make-up so they always look good.

First decide whether you are going for an unmade-up look or a dramatic effect – then choose your colours and products accordingly.

From the vast array available, choose the products you find easiest to use. Successful eye make-up relies on skilful application and it is much better not to be too adventurous at first until you are sure of the effect and have had enough time to practise.

Eye colours come in liquid, gel, powder or cream form; in bottles, tubes, pots, compacts, sticks or pencils. Pencils have made life a great deal easier for the average person as they are easy to control for shape and, being a cream formula, blend in well. A set of make-up brushes, sponges and combs will also be useful, keeping edges neat, eyelashes in place and applying products that don't come with their own applicator. It is essential to keep everything very clean, to avoid any possible irritation to the eyes.

Start with your chosen product on the lid, near the lashes and in the socket – draw the lines according to the shape of your eyes. How much lid shows, how much space you have between socket and brow, whether they are wide, deep- or close-set, all have a

Eyeliner
Draw with a pointed brush from inner to outer corner of upper lid. Make sure to apply it right into lash base. Don't flick it up at the end, just take a damp brush and soften the whole line by smudging the edge very gently (cake liners are best for this).

bearing on the placing of shadow – see pages 62–5 for how to over-come problems and make the best of your natural shape.

Next, use an eyeliner close to the lashes, or kohl pencil on the inner rims, if you are going to. This needs a steady hand or will look very messy. This is also the moment to use eyelash curlers, which, once you've mastered the instrument, are very useful – they make mascara application easier, open up the eyes and can create the illusion of longer, thicker lashes. It is very important not to pull eyelash curlers away from the lashes before fully opening the in-strument! Then highlight over the bone below the eyebrow – trans-parent skin tones are best for day in cream, pink or beige shades; keep high shine or metallic gleam for evening – and add a touch on the cheekbone below the outer corner of the eye.

If you have very sparse or short eyelashes you may like to add false ones. Whole strips are inclined to look very false, but a few single ones added to your own, particularly towards the outer corners, add thickness, length and can be very effective. Follow the directions exactly and, if you do use a strip, make sure it is well attached and isn't going to start lifting up at the corners.

The last step is mascara – easiest to apply is the wand, but it comes in cream or cake form too. Cream needs a good brush, as it is messy to use; the cake form usually comes with its own brush, is applied with water in several coats and is very efficient: it stays on well and the lashes don't clog. The technique for applying mascara is the same: first the top side of the upper lashes, stroking the colour down, then the underside of the top lashes, stroking the colour up, and lastly the lower lashes. Be careful there are no blobs of mascara left on the lashes and that they are well separated – a combined lash brush and comb is good – any colour that has touched the surrounding skin can be removed with a cotton bud. The best effect will be achieved with several light coats of mascara – this takes time but is well worth it.

Finally, look straight ahead into the mirror to check the shape you've made around your eyes; look closer to make sure everything is tidy – especially the inner corners of the eyes – and remove unwanted smudges of colour or flecks of powder with a cotton bud or sponge-stick applicator. Add a little depth to the colour in the socket if necessary – it may have soaked in a bit by this time. Brush eyebrows well to remove any trace of powder, up first, then across in the direction they grow. Then define with an eyebrow pencil if necessary – use soft, light feathery strokes and extend slightly at the ends. Lastly, brush again to blend in the pencil work. Eyebrows are an essential part of your facial character and provide a natural balance.

Fifth and Last Stage: Lips and Nails

After eyes, lips come close to being your most expressive feature. They are very mobile and sensual and your make-up must add to these qualities and never make them look stiff or dry. Fashion swings like a pendulum from lipsticks that are very dark through vivid bright colours to those that are closest to natural lip shades – and occasionally, as in the early sixties, to chalky pinks that are unnaturally pale and not very flattering, as they make the mouth look dry, but do draw attention to the eyes. One of the quickest ways to give yourself a new look is to reverse the focus you've been giving your face – for instance, if you've been wearing dark lipstick and not much eye make-up, try the opposite. This also gives you a chance to learn new make-up techniques, experiment with new products and avoid slipping into a make-up rut. Lip colours come in the conventional stick form, in tubes, compacts, pots or pencils; they range from opaque matt colours through shiny iridescent or pearlized shades to thin transparent tinted or colourless gloss. Again, pencils have made a terrific difference in helping people make up their lips successfully, but even better is to learn to use a lip brush. This way you get the cleanest possible outline – with colour filled in exactly where you want it and it should be – and, with practice you can learn the tricks that change the shape or emphasis of your mouth.

It's a good idea to have a small wardrobe of lip colours in products you find easy to use and a selection of clean brushes. When buying new colours, remember they will change when applied over your lips – a sensible place to test them is on the pad of a finger, which already has a pink tone.

When you start to make up your mouth, the outline of the lips should be rather obscure as your foundation and powder should have been blended over the edges. Outline first with a sharp pencil or lip brush in a colour that is a tone darker than the shade you're going to fill in with – you need a steady hand, so it's a good idea to rest your elbow on something solid. Then fill in with lip colour, either direct from the stick or using a lip brush. Blot, and apply another coat or add gloss – again with a lip brush; don't take the gloss right to the edges as it may cause the lipstick to run and ruin your clean outline.

Now stand away and look at yourself in a full-length mirror and check the balance of your make-up with your hair and clothes. This is particularly important for the shape of your mouth.

Don't forget how often your hands are seen in conjunction with your face – just because you've finished using them to apply your make-up doesn't mean you can dismiss them. Think how often you rest your chin on your hands, brush away a strand of hair or use your hands when you are talking. They are frequently closer to your face than you may realize.

Lipstick

Use a lip brush to put it on; powder around your mouth first (it minimizes 'bleeding'). Draw carefully and fill in with the brush or stick. Use lots of gloss. Steady your hand by resting your curled fingers on your chin. Don't make a hard different coloured line around your lips with a pencil or dark lipstick – it looks peculiar when the middle bit wears away.

You may not like nail colour, in which case nails should be buffed to a shine with special cream and a chamois leather nail buffer and the tips kept scrupulously clean and perhaps brightened underneath with a white nail pencil. If you do like nail colour, it needn't match your lip colour but should look pretty beside it whether toning or contrasting – and often the prettiest and most flattering to the hands of all are the beige or pale pink shades.

Nail polish, varnish or enamel come in bottles with their own applicator brushes and many companies offer colours that match or tone well with lipstick shades. Applying several thin coats, drying well in between and building up the colour is the best method and will prevent them chipping too soon.

However you choose to present your nails, they must be well manicured and cared for – bitten, broken or splitting nails, dry, frayed cuticles and hangnails and rough dry hands will ruin the effect of the most beautifully made-up face, hair and clothes. Hands are often a give-away on age, so to start treating them well early is an obvious investment in the future. The length and shape of nails varies with fashion and is also a question of life-style – someone who plays the piano, types or uses their hands a lot obviously cannot have long nails. Settle for nails that are all one length, healthy and well cared for – if they must be short, buff them or use a clear polish; if they are medium length, choose a colour that doesn't draw too much attention to them; don't make the mistake of ever growing them too long – talons are not attractive.

Highlighters
Apply after you have finished your make-up. Put them on with a brush and blend with your fingertips and anywhere you like, to make the skin look lively. Blend carefully so it doesn't 'sit' on the surface of the skin. Left side of face shows the action, right side, the effect.

28

Eric Boman

An A-Z of Equipment and Products

Applicators
Brushes that come with lip gloss, compacts of lipstick, powder blushers, powder eyeshadow; sponge-tipped sticks that come with powder or cream eyeshadows; spiral brushes that come with wand types of mascara; or tiny spatulas provided with foundation are all applicators. Your fingers are natural applicators.

Base
Also called foundation and sometimes 'make-up', this is tinted solid cream, liquid or gel designed to even out the skin tone, smooth the surface and provide a background for lip, eye and cheek colours.

Bleaching Cream
This lightens hair and is very useful for small patches of unwanted facial hair around lips etc.; if hair is very thick, dark or coarse, electrolysis is the best answer.

Blusher
Blusher is the modern term for rouge; it comes in cream form, stick or pencil, gel and powder. The creams, sticks and pencils are applied before powder; gel is best used without powder, as it's meant to give a transparent shine; the powder form is brushed on after face powder.

Brushes
Two or three brushes in different sizes, once you've mastered the art of using them, will help you give a professional touch to your

make-up. They give cleaner lines, blend colours better. Paint-brushes from an art shop are fine; you can also buy sets of cosmetic brushes, usually with some sponge and comb applicators as well.

Buffer
An oblong pad covered in chamois leather, a buffer is used with a buffing cream to bring a natural sheen to nails without the use of enamel.

Calamine Lotion
This is a tinted medicated liquid, very useful for soothing sunburn or itchy rashes or drying spots.

Combs
Tiny plastic combs are useful for separating eyelashes and smooth-ing eyebrows into line.

Concealer
This is an essential part of make-up. In stick or pencil or cream form, concealers come in various shades and are designed to cover discolouration or blemishes of any kind.

Cotton Buds
These are ideal for whisking away odd specks of coloured powder or mascara and generally tidying up make-up.

Cuticle Cream
This is a nourishing cream massaged into the cuticles and bases of the nail, to feed the nail where it grows and to keep the cuticles soft and separate from the nail.

Emery Boards
These are long spatulas covered in sand paper – medium-grained on one side, fine on the other – for filing finger- and toenails.

Eyelash Curlers

These are a scissors-like device for curling short or thin lashes. They should be used before mascara. A bit of practice is required: give just a gentle squeeze, which is enough to lift the lashes; be sure and open the scissors before taking the curlers off the lashes or you will pull them out; and don't re-curl after applying mascara – the mascara will stick to the curlers and pull out the lashes.

Eye Make-up

Any colour that you apply around your eyes counts as eye make-up: eyeshadows which come in cream, stick, liquid, gel or powder form; pencils, including kohl formulas for lining the rims; eyeliner; eyebrow pencils; mascara.

Eye Make-up Remover

This is a cleaner specifically designed to remove eye make-up efficiently. The eye and surrounding area are very sensitive and it is important that all make-up is thoroughly removed.

Fading Cream

This is a product designed to fade freckles and brown spots.

False Eyelashes

These can be bought in pairs (in various lengths and colours) or in long strips, from which you can take just one or two lashes and apply them individually.

False Fingernails

These are sold in sets, one for each fingernail, in various lengths and shapes. There is also a process, best done professionally, of wrapping the tips to extend them or of adding an acrylic substance

Three make-up stories on the following pages show step-by-step beauty including the skills of a make-up artist for the professional look, a fresh face for daytime and a make-up with shine and light for evening.

Eric Boman

1. *The face is covered with foundation and loose powder and the eyes are shaded and highlighted.* 2. *The model applies her own mascara, first brushing top lashes down and up, then lower lashes.* 3. *A dark shade of blusher is smoothed on with a brush.* 4, 5 *The blusher is blended to the desired strength with a small sponge and then the lipstick is applied.* 6. *The lips are carefully outlined before being filled in with a brush.*

Eric Boman

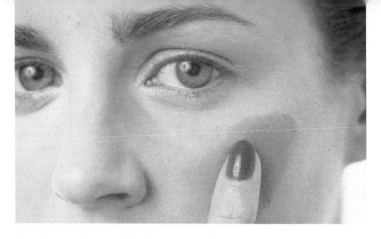

Step-by-step beauty for daytime make-up

First, smooth on a foundation neither too pale nor too tanned. Add blusher, then colour eyelids, dust over brow bones, softly rim lower lids with sponge applicator. Finish with mascara. Add shine to lips with lipgloss, over lipstick.

John Bishop

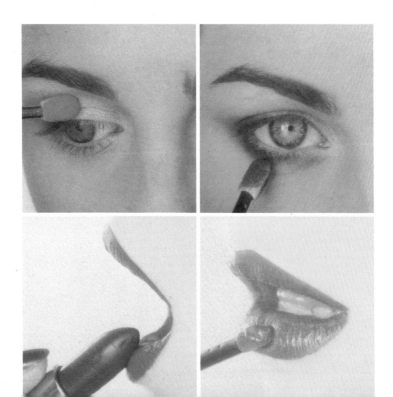

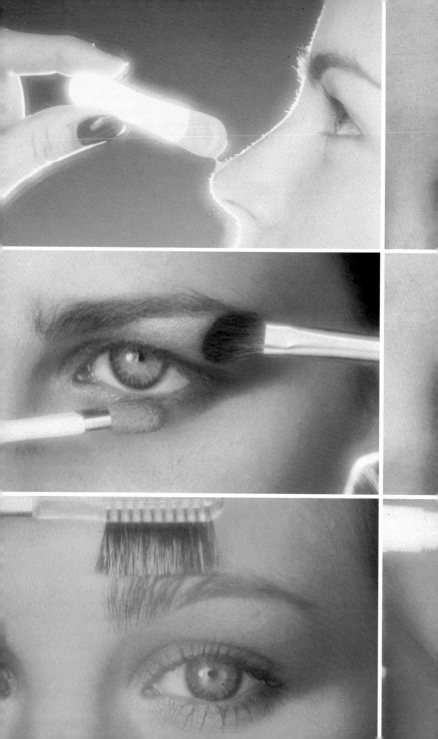

Step-by-step beauty for evening make-up

1. *Cleanse skin of all trace of day make-up and apply foundation by dotting over face.* *2.* *Blend with small light strokes.* **3 & 4.** *With a new set of brushes apply soft clear colouring for eyes, outlining them and shading upper lids.* **5.** *Tidy brows with eyebrow brush and comb. Apply final light touches with tulip pink blusher and translucent powder.* *6.* *Paint lips, colour cheeks and complete make-up with a light dusting of powder.*

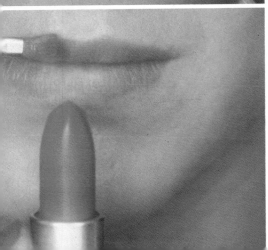

John Bishop

that hardens and is then filed into shape and painted. Either method is excellent for one or two broken nails, or for those who have problems getting their nails to grow at all.

Foundation
This is merely another term for base or 'make-up'.

Hand Cream
This is an essential lubricant to prevent the hands drying and ageing prematurely. It should be used every time hands have been immersed in water and dried.

Highlighter
This is one of a girl's most valuable make-up accessories. Shiny, pearlized, iridescent, full of gold or silver – whether they are liquid, powder or cream, they bring life to the face when applied with care on places such as browbones and cheekbones.

Kohl
This is a powder used by Ancient Egyptians and Greeks not only for painting lines around eyes but also for darkening eyebrows and lashes. North African kohl is still a powder applied to the inner rims of the eyes with a rod. The Indian equivalent is a cream called kajal. Modern cosmetic products called kohl are usually in pencil form, in many colours and intended for colouring the inner rims of the eyes.

Lip Barrier
This is an emollient stick, often containing sunscreen, used to moisturize and prevent lips chapping.

Lip Colour
Lipsticks, lip pencils and lip gloss are all kinds of lip colour. All three add colour, lipsticks usually matt or frosted, lip pencils helping the

drawing of a clean outline and lip gloss adding shine, transparent or tinted.

Make-up Remover and Cleanser
It is vital to the continuing good condition of your skin that make-up is removed thoroughly; these items, with a special version for eye make-up, are essential.

Mascara
This is colour, found either in cake form, which is applied to the lashes with a brush and water, or in a creamy wand with its own applicator. The creamy varieties sometimes contain filaments which adhere to the lashes, making them appear thicker. All mascaras should make lashes look darker, thicker and more luxuriant; to achieve this, it is much better to apply several coats, separating the lashes carefully between each coat so they don't get clogged.

Mirror
Many people find a large hand mirror with a magnifier one side enormously helpful, particularly for plucking eyebrows and applying eye make-up. In any case, a large mirror surrounded by good even light is essential if your make-up isn't going to look uneven.

Nail Pencil
This is a pencil filled with white which cleans the tips of the nails and makes them look much brighter, when coloured polish isn't being worn.

Nail Polish
Also called varnish or enamel, nail polish is found in every colour of the rainbow from transparent to blood red, purple and black. It is best applied in several thin coats and allowed to dry completely in between.

Orange Sticks
These are used for gently pushing back cuticles and helping cuticle cream to penetrate underneath – a good trick is to round the edge with a penknife to soften it. They are helpful too in cleaning up smudges of polish when you've finished your manicure or pedicure.

Pencil Sharpeners
Now that so many eye, cheek and lip colours come in pencil form (from slim to chunky), it's vital to have them sharp at all times to make sure the wood doesn't snag the skin. So, keep sharpeners of the right size in your make-up bag – and clean the blade with surgical spirit.

Powder
Face powder comes in many tints but is most popular now in a colourless translucent form, used to 'set' make-up not to add colour. Keep loose powder on the dressing-table and carry a compact of pressed powder around with you.

Sponges
These are used for applying cream or stick foundation – they should be dampened first. Tiny sponge-tipped applicators for eyeshadow are also useful.

Tweezers
These are essential for keeping eyebrows tidy. Only pluck from below and be careful not to take out too many hairs at once – eyebrows add a great deal of character to the face and it's easy to overdo it.

Zinc
This is used in medicated lip ointments.

The Right Light:
What a Difference It Makes

The right light is vital to successful make-up. Light can play strange tricks with its strength and shadows and this can be used to your advantage provided you are aware of it. Blinking disco lights can do wonderful, strange things to the colours and contours of your face; you can use bright glittering colours to great effect – but beware of looking grotesque; soft candlelight is the most flattering of all, throwing flickering shadows and a mellow smoothness that few faces possess on their own; clear daylight can be soft or, with bright sun, very harsh.

The important thing is to accept the basic structure of your face and make the most of it. Make-up tricks to change its shape or contours must never be obvious or they create no illusion and lose their point.

Light changes colours, affects tone and depth. It also changes shape. A trick of the light can make an older face look younger or vice versa. Photographers can flatter their subjects with a light that smooths out lines or choose one that records every blemish. The same make-up will look different in daylight, sunlight, twilight or nightlight.

In summertime or in bright sunshine, pale colours look stronger and many people look best with no foundation – just a moisturizer or sunscreen plus very light eyeshadow, mascara, lip gloss (blusher for pale faces only). Nightlight needs stronger make-up. Start with moisturizer, then foundation to even the skin tone, outline lips with a pencil and dust over lots of loose face powder – the trick here is to use much more than you would expect and to dust off the excess; this way the matt look lasts longer. Next, contour your face with a powder blusher – use a darker shade in the hollows of the cheeks, perhaps around the eyes and temples. Shine on the eyes and lips reflects nightlight, makes the eyes look bright; also use lots of mascara and a dark pencil in the sockets and around the lashes for definition. Even a bright lip colour can fade away at night so give your mouth a sharp outline with the pencil. Experiment with an iridescent highlighter, turning your head to see how it catches the light and where it is most flattering to you – the centre of the eyelid, the browbone, down the bridge of the nose, cheekbones, in the crease of the upper lips, the cleft of the chin are good places to try.

Electric light is incandescent, very even, and you need definite colours … real reds for lips, russet, soft green or blue for eyes.

Neon light is harsh; avoid pale lips and greys and browns which hollow out the cheeks. Choose warm tones: tangerine, shocking pink, gilded, pearlized corals. Outline the edge of your lips, and try iridescent rose, bronze or copper around the eyes.

Candlelight is most flattering, providing you're not sunburned. Avoid orange lips, hard eyes. Shape your face softly. Use lots of blusher. Soften, blush, lengthen the eye. For lips try muted blue-reds or wine shades and matt mauve, prune or grape for eyes.

The first essential is to see your face in the right light. Make up in the light you are going to be seen by, if at all possible. If you are going out in daylight, try and apply your make-up in the nearest equivalent – take a good mirror to a window, prop the mirror against it so that all the light falls on your face. Don't choose harsh direct sunlight or you may be tempted to use too heavy a hand and end up looking over made-up. For evenings, make up by electric light – then check the effect in softer light, candlelight, for instance, or a lower watt bulb. Place yourself in electric light in the same way as daylight – at a dressing-table or in a bathroom, for instance – and try and arrange light to fall on your face from all angles (side lights slightly in front of you and any overhead light falling on your face, not the back of your neck). Don't make up in bad light and, above all, don't make up where the source of light only falls on one side of your face. This will only mean your make-up ends up looking uneven or lop-sided.

Make sure you are comfortable and try and leave more than enough time for the job so that you are relaxed and don't run the risk of making time-consuming mistakes. First pin hair out of the way to expose your face – if you are using heated rollers or setting it in any way, this is a good moment to save time. Make sure your skin is scrupulously clean, then apply a moisturizer. It's a good idea to leave it a while to sink in, otherwise your foundation may slip around too much. Use this time to assemble all the colours you are planning to use before starting – this avoids the sudden discovery of a missing favourite lip or eye colour on which your whole make-up idea was based and the necessity of starting all over again.

The Weather:
How It Affects Your Looks

How do you make your looks weather the weather? No one wants their make-up to run when the temperature soars, their hair to look a mess when the humidity is rising or the sun to make their skin resemble a peeled chestnut. Travelling, for most people, means more time in the sun or outdoors and although a bit of tan makes almost everyone look more vital and alive, over-exposure to sun is something you pay for with toughened, parched skin that will age faster, and dry brittle hair. These tips should help you plan your travelling beauty bag so that you look great wherever you are.

When it's winter – at home or abroad – protect skin from rain and cold. If you're a soap-and-water person, switch to a milder soap, less frequent washing and consider using a cream cleanser as an alternative. Don't wash your face immediately before going out in the cold – it's too drying and you risk chapping. Do it at least half an hour before and let the moisturizer sink in well. Cold reduces the elasticity of the skin and less humidity in the air makes for dryness, so you need to pay more attention to moisturization, which provides a protective barrier between the skin and the elements. Cold-weather activities – skiing, skating or a brisk walk – may work up a sweat and so increase chances of skin chapping. Lips need protecting; make sure the area around mouth and chin is well moisturized. Moisturizer should contain a good effective sunscreen. Sunglasses should be worn to prevent squinting in bright light, which encourages lines. Moisturizing glossy lip colours are the ones to look for and apply over a sunproofed lip protector and waterproof mascara.

In summer, your metabolism is speeded up and oil glands are more active, so change your moisturizer to something light and apply a sunscreen every morning before you make up. Try a tinted sunscreen to give you a healthy glow, with just mascara and lip colour.

Long-distance travellers often notice their nails become brittle, skin becomes very dry or unusually greasy, hair becomes oily. A lot of problems encountered by air-travellers are caused by dehydration en route – this can be counteracted by drinking lots of water during the trip. Take a nail strengthener and cuticle cream with you – a long air journey offers a terrific opportunity for a really good manicure – and lots of moisturizing hand cream. And, take a mild shampoo and a separate conditioner so that you can wash your hair as often as it needs and regulate your conditioning to the climate.

Be aware that the condition of your skin will change as climate changes. A cleanser or moisturizer that works in warm weather may not be rich enough in winter; if you go by plane, take some with you and apply during the journey.

You'll find *humidity plus air pollution* in cities like Rome, New York, Tel Aviv and Tokyo and you may find your skin looks dingy and your make-up fades as soon as you put it on. Air pollution can cause eye irritations that give you a puffy red-eyed look.

Use a good eyedrop designed to reduce redness, then lie down and apply cotton pads saturated with witch-hazel to your eyes. If you can put the witch-hazel in the refrigerator to cool it, it's especially refreshing. And, if witch-hazel isn't immediately to hand, try slices of cucumber or potato – old-fashioned remedies, but effective.

In cities like New York, for instance, the combination of cold, dry outdoor air and hot dry indoor air is very hard on skin and make-up. Dry skin can chap and develop an uneven texture. If you can, invest in a humidifier for indoors, use a richer moisturizer, and use

Patrick Demarchelier

a moisturizing foundation with good coverage to add a protective barrier.

You'll find *very dry and hot weather* in places like Marrakesh, Baalbeck, the Gulf and on the Nile. Your lips may become parched and cracked and you'll probably have trouble making make-up go on smoothly. Laugh lines may seem more prominent. The big enemy to your looks in this environment is sun and, of course, its effects are intensified in the summer months. Protect your hair with a scarf, your skin with effective sunscreens and choose cream varieties of eye colour, blusher and moisturizing lipsticks.

You'll find *tropical heat and humidity* in Bangkok, Fiji or the Seychelles, for instance, and you may feel your make-up is melting as soon as you've put it on. The increased heat and humidity cause oil glands to be more active and the oil to be more fluid, so that it mixes with perspiration more. This tends to cause break-outs and unexpected rashes. Choose a foundation formulated for oily skins – this will help the rest of your make-up stay on your skin too – or try using a bronze-tinted sunscreen to give your skin a sunny glow.

Take a soothing medicated lotion to treat spots and a camouflage stick for dry blemishes. You'll probably find that powder eyeshadows and blushers stay on best; choose lipsticks with staying power and matt textures, slicking gloss on top to lighten the effect.

Expert Make-up for Different Skin Colourings

Very fair skins and spun-sugar silvery blond hair, epitomized by Scandinavian good looks, need the greatest possible care in make-up. The skin tends to be delicate, often very sensitive and dry and must always be protected from the sun. Moisturizer is essential at all times and should always be used under foundation. Only the lightest foundation is needed to achieve a smooth creamy texture which is the first step to porcelain pink-and-white looks; alternatively a gel make-up gives a tinge of honey colour that is very attractive but almost impossible to acquire safely from the sun. A light hand is the golden rule for fair good looks – experiment with almost any colour you like, but stick to the lightest shades.

The prettiest natural look for daytime is to make the most of the eyes, shadowing them in neutral colours that blend with the eyes, intensifying with kohl and mascara, shining lips with gloss, and just a hint of blush. In the evening a beautiful purity can be the answer – rose pink lips and cheeks, grey eyes highlighted with pink and gold, for instance.

Natural blondes, and particularly *dark blondes*, often have a lot of red in their hair colour; their skin tends to burn easily and freckle, like redheads. But they can take stronger colours than the very fair and have more choice than redheads. They are often considered the lucky ones – any colour looks good on them. However, their skin is likely to be on the dry side and they should be careful using strong colours as their make-up should never be harsh.

It's easy to look washed-out wearing bright colours, but if you're fair-skinned and blond, be careful not to look over made-up. Choose a light-textured foundation (which allows your skin to show through) in a shade nearest your skin tone (test on the side of your jaw and choose in good daylight). Smoky colours – plum, grey, green, blue – look good around the eyes; use a pink to plum blusher and true pink or real red lipsticks.

Redheads with their tendency to beautiful translucent skin often have freckles too. The skin only has a small amount of melanin (the pigment that turns skin brown) in it and this means they burn easily or acquire freckles, which come from irregular pigmentation. Freckles don't appear only on the face but often all over the body – particularly across the shoulders. All freckles tend to fade during the winter but return as soon as the sun shines on the skin again. You can't stop them appearing, but a really good sunscreen will minimize them.

The best make-up results will come from learning to love your freckles and make the most of natural healthy colouring – only covering up for a specific smooth look in the evening. Freckles can be a terrific asset – many girls paint on fake ones for a healthy effect – so use a bronze gel base or just a moisturizing sunscreen during the day and a more covering foundation in the evening if you like.

With very pale, almost white eyelashes, it's worth considering having them dyed from time to time. Most salons do this, requiring a patch test twenty-four hours in advance to make sure you have no bad reaction; it is quite simple and makes a great difference to your looks. Otherwise, use lots of coats of mascara.

Natural colours for cheeks and lips are the tawny shades – peach, sienna, copper, bronze and terracotta – with rust, green and

On the following eight pages are illustrations of suggested make-ups for different colourings.

Eric Boman

▲ Patrick Demarchelier

Albert Watson ▶

overleaf Lothar Schmid

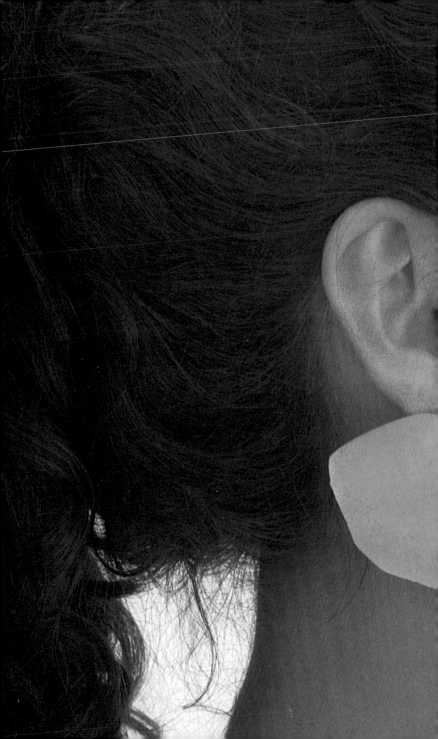

◄ *Eric B*
Parkins

apricot tones around the eyes. Iridescents are great in the evening and gold is the redhead's natural highlighter, but stay away from silver. If you want to be more adventurous, play up either eyes *or* lips with a surprise colour but not both at once. Try violet or orchid pink around the eyes, shocking pink or raspberry lips.

Orientals often have creamy skin (with the tone ranging from pale ivory to warm olive) and black hair. This can look wonderful with really strong bright lips and smudgy charcoal eyes.

Brunettes with olive skin may find a mauve tinted moisturizer helpful in reducing any sallowness in the skin and often look best in earth tones for lips and cheeks – the darker your skin the more dramatic the colour can be; paler skins should stick to a softer look. Try green, bronze, brown around the eyes and highlight with creamy gold.

Girls with dark skins and dark brown or black hair often complain their skins are greasy and their make-up too shiny. This normally begins to disappear in their thirties, but then the danger is that the skin often goes very dry and, if neglected or not cleaned meticulously, may develop a grey or ashy look.

Dark skins need little or no tinted foundation or powder as they usually have a natural bloom and good all-over tone, but, if patchy, make-up can help to even out the tone; often a gel-bronze foundation is all that is needed. Red or yellow tints of foundation are not usually flattering – cool brown and earthy shades are best – and the gel or liquid varieties rather than stick or cream are usually most satisfactory.

Blushers in brick or wine shades (it's usually better to avoid light pink or red) and lipsticks in earth tones or wine are most becoming. Girls with the lighter types of brown skin can look wonderful with the brilliance of a true red or cyclamen pink. Pearlized lipsticks are inclined to make a mouth look larger; well-defined mouths usually look best with a minimum of colour, just glossed.

For eye make-up, avoid pearly colours if lids or the eye area is at all puffy. Where lids are narrow, a pearlized gel can help to shape the lid. If lashes are on the short side, a narrow band of cream or bone colour on the lid can give the illusion of more length. Kohl on the inner rims is very effective, as is lots of mascara. Good colour palettes to choose from are green through copper and bronze to golden brown and deep blue through plum to smoky grey.

Black skins have many variations in shade from mahogany to almost black; and normally tend to be oily. But, if exposed to a cold climate, many black skins suffer from dryness too. These complexions can burn in the sun, though not as severely as paler skins. Well-conditioned black skin should appear smooth and burnished and of an even tone – a greyish sheen means it's suffering from dryness or the wrong shade of foundation is being used.

Foundations and powders formulated for white skins are often not suitable for black, because they contain ingredients to deposit the greyish sheen mentioned above or a too red or too yellow tone. Many black skins, because of their oily texture, suffer from enlarged pores and, if exposed to cold and suffering from dryness, need moisturizing protection. Therefore, the choice of foundation is a vital one for successful make-up – a tinted moisturizer or bronzing gel may give just the right amount of coverage to protect and even out the skin tone, but if a heavier coverage is required, the base must be selected with great care. Most cosmetic ranges have dark shades of foundation and powder specially formulated for black skins, and there are cosmetic ranges specifically for black girls too.

The trick is to improve the natural polish of black skin. The use of highlighter (transparent white or a pink one with gold in it) above cheekbones, just above the upper lip, down the bridge of the nose and around the eye area is particularly effective. Use sparingly and let the natural skin show through the surface sheen. Transparency is the prettiest effect to aim at, no matter how much colour you choose to apply. Thin cheek gels in copper, wine or even magenta; and lip gloss, over a matt colour if you like, ranging from coral, brick, plum and brandy shades to the darkest wine and blackberry are good products to experiment with. For eyes, all the iridescent products are perfect – for a neutral make-up, shade in gold, apricot and rust, or amethyst, rose and burgundy, depending on the particular tone of your skin; for evening or for fun, try the peacock blues, greens, purples with silver or gold highlight. Add kohl pencil inside the lower rim and lots of mascara in several coats, separating the lashes as you go.

A good rule is to stay away from muddy colours and experiment with the clear vivid ones that look harsh on paler complexions.

Expert Make-up for the Woman over Thirty-five

When forty starts approaching many women panic – they start rushing off to plastic surgeons to discuss face-lifts only to be told they are much too young and not to return for several years. Forty is *not* the beginning of the end; a few lines certainly don't mean the whole face is disintegrating; and a bit of overweight can be removed, even though it may take longer.

All that is really needed is a beauty reassessment, a re-think of make-up, hair style and colour. In order to maintain energy, healthy hair and skin, more attention must be paid to exercise and diet – the effects of years of careless diet and body neglect will start to show in the thirties; from then on, weight-control is much harder and it takes more effort and longer to improve skin and hair health.

The body needs more help to function efficiently; the skin is beginning to lose its elasticity, hair may lose its colour and texture, and make-up needs a different approach.

Around forty is when many women who have never had a skin problem in their lives discover the distress of specific forms of acne, psoriasis, blackheads, whiteheads and enlarged pores. Brown spots can appear and don't disappear – these can now be minimized by regular use of special fading creams. Skin colour can change or go patchy and this discolouration is often due to sluggish circulation – exercise or a brisk walk will improve the tone and a soft cream or fluid foundation in the correct shade will do the rest. If there are broken veins or blemishes to hide, use a camouflage cream or stick.

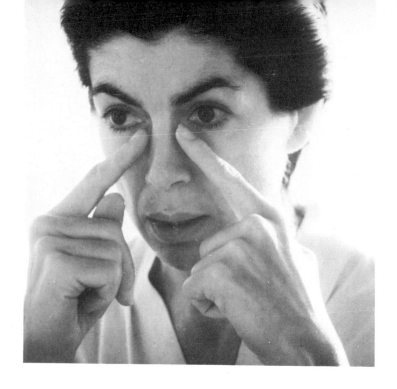

Aim to look well, rather than slavishly using the latest fashion colours to look trendy. A light hand with make-up is essential – heavy make-up is ageing, as are dark colours and hard lines.

Choose a foundation to improve your natural tone – perhaps with a little extra pink or peach in it. Avoid cool beiges unless you have a naturally high colour, in which case a mud beige will act as camouflage, and try a green tinted moisturizer underneath. Skin shouldn't look too powdered – or shine too much, although this is unlikely as most skins dry out as they get older. Too matt a finish looks lifeless, so be particularly careful not to use powdery make-up or powder under the eyes or on the area of the browbone. Powder sinks into every slight imperfection, is bad for delicate skin and makes the eyes look lifeless. Use translucent powder – a neutral colour or just a shade lighter than your foundation – and fluff it on

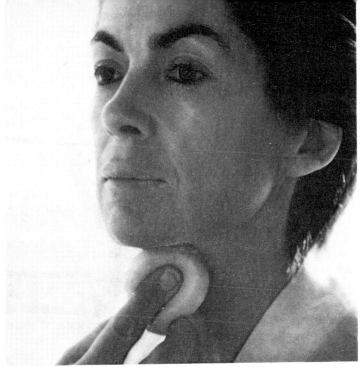

Sandra Lousada

very lightly with a puff. Be careful on lines running from nose to mouth – they are the first place foundation and powder sink into, giving a tired impression.

Use blusher sparingly – if it is very well blended it is flattering, but beware of adding to an already high skin tone and looking feverish.

Beware of iridescent eye make-up – shine can emphasize the smallest blemish. And avoid very bright colours; a shade several tones paler than your eye colour is often a good guide. The varieties of eyeshadow that are painted on with water (a dampened sponge-applicator) are often the most satisfactory as they last better and don't settle into the creases, although many of the newer cream formulas are excellent. Avoid dark eyeliners; use soft smoky green, blue or grey and smudge a line near the lashes.

Don't be tempted by gold, silver or glitter – they will just draw attention to everything you are trying to minimize. Eyebrows need to be kept trim – neither too thin nor too prominent. Always pluck from below and never use a hard dark pencil. If your brows have thinned, use a soft grey or brown pencil and make light feathery strokes. Aim at keeping the whole eye area moist and soft-looking, neither too dry or powdery nor so shiny that the creases are very evident. If your eyelids tend to droop at the outer corner, keep eyeliner and shadow 'lifted', with slightly more depth of shadow towards the temple. Don't make obvious lines and don't extend the make-up beyond the corner of the eye unless it is very carefully blended. A touch of highlighter immediately below the brow is a good idea. So is mascara, but choose dark brown or grey rather than hard black. A special eye make-up remover is a good investment as it whisks away all the colour with minimum disturbance.

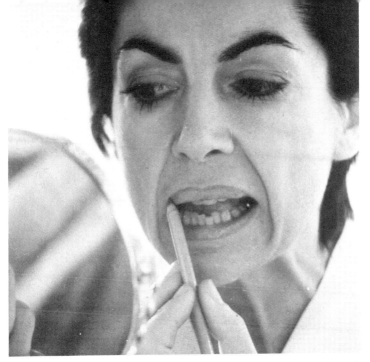

Sandra Lousada

Cream your lips at night to keep them soft and blot carefully before putting on lipstick. A good tip is to take your foundation over the edge of your lips, powder well, then outline with a lip pencil or lip brush, fill in with colour, blot again and powder again. This helps to maintain a clean outline and avoids the colour 'bleeding' into the tiny lines around the mouth. Choose a lipstick colour that is light and creamy.

Pinks, corals and light reds are most becoming – but it's worth experimenting with the plum shades. Pale lipstick will make the lips look dry, brighter ones add life to the skin and eyes. Iridescent colours will show up every tiny line – matt creamy shades, with just a touch of extra gloss if you like, are much more flattering.

If the mouth tends to droop at the corners, extend the outline of the lower lip upwards and don't take the colour on the top lip all the way into the corner.

Colour Co-ordination: What to Wear with What

There are dozens of choices in terms of the colours you like to wear and the colours you put on your face. And the little thing that can make the most excitement and change in your looks is a new make-up colour – a new blusher, lipstick, eyeshadow or whatever. It doesn't mean you need a new make-up colour for every piece of clothing, but it does mean choosing your make-up within the spectrum of colours that suit your hair and skin tone *and* the colours you choose to wear, so that the overall effect is in harmony from top to toe. Each colour you choose to wear or put on your face should enhance the others and flatter your skin, hair and eyes. Sometimes it's fun to keep eyes, lips and cheeks the same colour as the dress you're wearing – pink, for instance – but this needs expert application to be really effective.

White, cream, beige, brown, grey, black – these are the neutral colours which suit almost everyone; make-up should then be in clear colours to flatter hair and skin. At night, gold and silver highlight is very effective with frosted lipsticks and cheek colours.

Yellow, orange, tan – these are sometimes difficult to wear as they are inclined to reflect on to the skin and give a sallow impression. They are good with a tan and redheads look wonderful in these colours – others are often wise to put white, cream, beige or grey between them and their face. Peach or tawny blushers work best, with peach, coral, vermilion, sienna and rust for lips. On eyes try moss green, bronze, golden or smoky browns – brown mascara is softer than black – and highlight in gold.

Green – from pale almond to forest, this is the natural colour for redheads but good on blondes and brunettes too, particularly anyone with hazel or green eyes. Green can make pale skins look paler, so it might be a good idea to use a warmer shade of foundation and make sure your blusher is in the apricot to tawny group. Try bois de rose, crimson, light red or russet lipstick and shade eyes with apricot and teal green, smoky greens, copper or try mauve with clear green kohl lining the inner rim.

Blue – from sky through violet to navy and purple, this is probably the most popular colour in the rainbow; some form suits almost everyone. Like green it can make pale skins look paler, so check your foundation shade. Russet or rose pink blusher looks pretty; for lips try all the pinks from pastel peach to shocking and magenta and true red. Don't try for a perfect match on your eyes, but keep them in the same family – the smoky blues and violets are more flattering than the light chalky shades – or try apricot, copper and brown.

Red – this cheers anyone up; a touch is often enough and could just be your lipstick. With bright red lips, keep eyes neutral – charcoal is great and bronze is interesting with red, if lips are pale and glossy.

Pink – this ranges from rose to fuchsia, crimson and wine. Light clear pinks are among the most flattering colours to wear, but when you get into the crimson and wine shades, be sure your make-up doesn't appear muddy. Choose clear bright lipsticks in the same family and pink cheeks; try grey, smoky blue, plum or orchid pink on the eyes and pink highlighter.

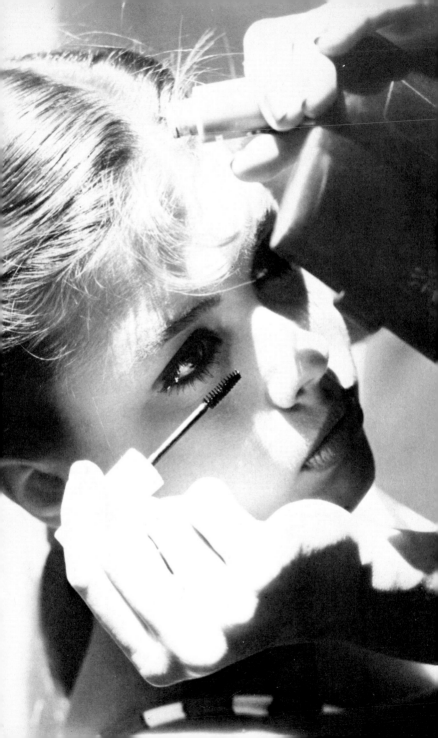

Your Face:
How to Change Its Shape

Play up your good points, minimize the bad and proceed with caution. Too often contouring and highlighting is done with a heavy hand and the result is grotesque, but with extreme care much can be done with make-up to improve the basic shape of your face, eyes or lips.

First, face your problems – look at yourself in a really good light and work out the shape of your face, what you like about it and what you don't. Next, look at your eyes – are they wide- or close-set? Narrow, protruding or too round? Do your lids droop or do your brows overhang? Are your eyebrows too heavy or an untidy shape? Now, your lips – are they too full, too narrow or uneven?

Take your face first and, using the principle of light and shade, decide what you are going to emphasize and what you want to diminish. The upper line of the cheekbone, the browbone, the temples, the ridge of the nose, the centre of the upper lip and the centre of the chin are all good places to try and highlight. A wide nose, heavy jaw and cheek hollows are places to experiment with shading – use a darker tone of foundation or one of the special contour powders or creams described as 'face-shapers'. With both light and shade, use very little to start with and build up until you achieve the effect you want; this will take some time and a lot of patience.

Now eyes. If they are wide-set you are fortunate, but if they are too close together they will appear farther apart if you apply a deep, smoky tone of shadow to the outer corners of the eyelid, blending

(*Continued on page 70*)

Changing the Shape
of Your Face

Widen Your Eyes

Eyes that have too much lid showing should be coloured across the entire lid, into the crease and halfway across lower lid and then blended as shown.

Widen Your Eyes

*Eyes that are set too close together can be widened by drawing a trian-
gular shape with an eye pencil from the outer corners, halfway across
both upper and lower lids and crease. Then blend as shown.*

64

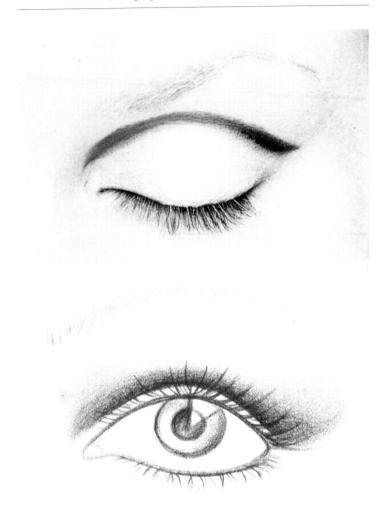

Open Your Eyes

Eyes with little lid showing and lots of space and bone need a light eyeshadow on the lid, a dark line drawn in the crease then blended up and out.

Reshape Your Face

To slim the bridge of your nose take a paintbrush and a cream foundation about three shades deeper than your skin tone and draw a small triangle at the inner end of the brows. Blend carefully.

To slim the lower part of your nose, paint a small elongated triangle vertically above the nostrils, then blend carefully.

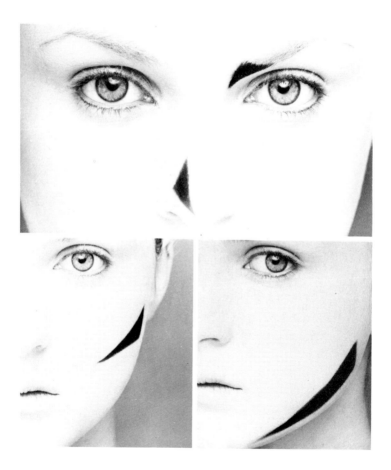

To slim the jawline, paint a long wedge shape just above the edge then blend carefully. Use a cream foundation about three shades darker than your skin, but not a red tone. To raise the cheekbones, draw elongated triangles just below the bones, fill in and blend.

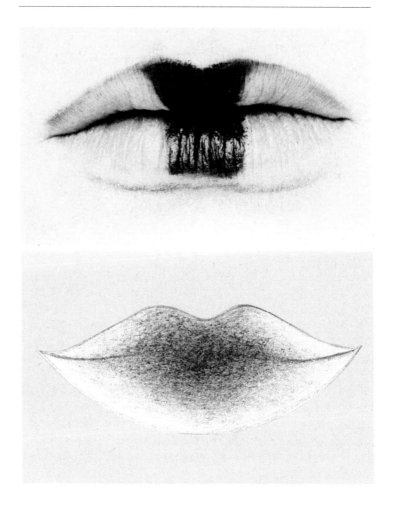

Balance Your Lips

If your lips are too full take a lip pencil and outline the centre of the top lip, then fill in the centre section of both lips, with a darker colour lipstick than your chosen shade. Blend as shown in drawing.

If your upper lip is narrow, paint a line with a pencil just over the top lip edge, fill in the upper lip with lipstick, and use a lighter shade on lower lip.

it up towards the end of your eyebrow and just under the lower lashes. If they are narrow, try applying dark shadow close to the lashes, from the centre of the lower lashes round the outer corner across the top to the inner corner. Smudge for a soft effect. If eyes protrude, they will appear less prominent if you draw a band of colour right round the eye close to the lashes in a medium to deep shade. A pencil is good for this; smudge it lightly so the line isn't too hard. If eyes are too round, elongate them by shading two thirds of the upper lid (the outer section) and blending it upward to the brow and just under the outer corner.

Droopy lids will appear less sleepy if colour follows the natural shape of the eye; widen the band towards the outer corner and blend it outwards and upwards, with a little colour under the eye for balance. Overhanging brows can be lifted if you apply shadow from the inside corner of the eye over the top lid, then around the outer corner and bottom lid; smudge for a soft outline.

If you feel your eyebrows are too heavy and decide to pluck them yourself, take great care not to overdo it and remove a lot of the character from your face. Never pluck the top line and never cut them – only pluck from below, a few hairs at a time.

If you feel your eyebrows are too thin and sparse or too pale, use an eyebrow pencil. If it is depth you need, choose a brown or grey colour, but if it is just added line that's required, choose a colour to match your own brows. Either way, start near the bridge of the nose and work outwards, using soft feathery strokes and extending them slightly at the outer edge.

Lips that are too full will look smaller if you use a light shade of lipstick and concentrate the colour on the centre section. Thin lips will look fuller if the outline is drawn *just* outside the edges and they are filled in with colour and gloss. Uneven lips can be better balanced if two tones of colour, plus gloss, are used – use the lighter tone and gloss on the narrow lip and leave the fuller one darker and matt. Lips that droop at the corners and give a sad expression can be tilted by extending the outline of the lower lip at the corners.

Barry Lategan

Hands and Feet:
How to Add the Final Touch

Beautifully kept hands, soft and smooth with strong well-shaped nails all one length are quickly noticed. Equally quickly noticed are dry, blistered, wrinkled ones with bitten, dirty or split nails. In summer or on holiday, feet are exposed to the same sort of scrutiny and toenails are as noticeable as fingernails, needing just as much year-round care.

Feet work enormously hard for their living – they take the full weight of your body and their condition can affect the way you feel each day. Everyone knows the facial expression (and feel) of pain that comes from ill-fitting shoes, corns, blisters or just feet that have walked too far and aren't used to it. Problem feet can be due to a variety of causes, including heredity, ill-fitting shoes, poor posture and fatigue. Flat-footedness and a predisposition to bunions caused by the first toe being shorter than the second seem to be inherited. But many other problems are the result of foot abuse – expecting the foot to carry all kinds of weight in all sorts of footwear over all kinds of surface without any care or maintenance at all.

It's an excellent idea to have a professional manicure and pedicure from time to time, but in between set aside a regular hour or so at least once a week for hands and feet – and start with your feet because you'll need your hands to work on them; then they can rest and the polish can dry while you attend to your hands.

How to Choose your Nail Colour
First, examine carefully the shape of your hands, feet and the condition of your nails – but consider each separately.

First your hands – if you are fortunate enough to have been born with really beautifully shaped hands and fingers and have nourished and cared for your nails, you can choose virtually any colour of the rainbow as polish. They run from brown, russet and plum ... to the pale pretty pinks and shocking ... to the vibrant poster-paint primaries, blue, green, yellow ... and all the true brilliant reds. If you have great nails, polish them bright.

The very pale, opaque, ivory or bone shades, and the harsh iridescent or very dark colours are more eye-catching than medium tones. So, if you feel your hands leave a bit to be desired in the way of shape but your nails are in good condition, choose mid-tone corals and pinks that blend naturally with your clothes and make-up.

But, however good or bad the shape of your hands, if your nails are broken, bitten or unsightly, forget colour and put your effort towards repairing them. Buff them to a natural shine – this also stimulates circulation, and blood feeds the matrix where the nail grows – or paint them with a clear natural polish which will help protect and strengthen them.

Tips to Remember when Painting Nails

The prettiest nail is filed into a soft oval, the cuticle massaged away and loosened off the nail, the skin kept soft with hand cream.

Start by filing nails, properly, with the fine side of an emery board, always towards the centre. Never file them into points or down into the corners.

If you paint the colour down the side of the nails, it tends to broaden their appearance, so only do this if they are long and narrow.

If nails incline to be broad, leave the last tiny strip on either side clear.

If nails are slim, they may look good with the moons left clear, but this also has a widening effect, so if they are the slightest bit square, cover the moons.

If you decide on half-moons, the first stroke of colour should be taken across from one side of the moon's edge to the other; they need a very steady hand for a good effect, so unless you've had plenty of practice, leave it to a professional manicurist.

Before you start painting, be sure your nails are absolutely clean – after removing obvious dirt, a white pencil run under the nail tip brightens the tone.

For soft nails, or those that are flaking, a nail hardener will help and a base coat or protective top coat will lengthen the life of your chosen nail colour.

The best way to remove old polish is to wet a cotton pad with remover, hold it on the nail for a minute to pre-soften the polish and wipe off slowly. Then, most important, wash hands and around nails thoroughly to take off the remover.

A weekly manicure is plenty; too frequent use of remover weakens your nails' natural strength. Remover is largely acetone and excessive use of it can cause the essential cementing ingredients to dry out, which causes splitting nails. It's better to touch up polish between manicures rather than remove it every time there's a chip. Buy oil-based remover – it's less drying.

Putting on Polish

Prime with a base coat to prevent chipping. Allow it to dry, then apply several coats of polish, drying each coat before applying the next. Last, put on a top coat for added strength. Delicate nails can benefit from nail hardeners applied to just the free, unattached edge.

Apply polish with decisive strokes from the base of the nail to the tip – make sure you don't get too much polish on the brush or you will get blobs on the nail and be tempted to go back and smooth them out. Three thin coats will give a much smoother result than one thick one – and will last much longer.

The bright, vivid shine of polish is a nice finishing touch for toenails, especially in summer – or whenever you wear sandals.

Pick a good basic colour that will go with many things, so you won't have to change polish too often. Polish should last two weeks.

Again foot condition, foot shape and the health of their nails must influence your choice of colour, but generally speaking a bright clear red, rust or magenta looks prettiest. With open-toed shoes or sandals, don't forget that your feet are very much a part of your top-to-toe appearance and the colour of your toenails should blend or contrast deliberately with the colours you are wearing.

Twelve Steps to a Professional Pedicure

First assemble your equipment – most of these things last quite a long time and are useful for your manicure or other parts of your beauty routine, so it's not such a daunting, expensive list as it may first appear:

nail polish remover, cottonwool, tissues, a bowl large enough for both your feet to rest in comfortably when filled with warm, soapy water (a mild shampoo is ideal, don't use detergent), a towel, nail brush, pumice stone, emery board, orange sticks, cuticle cream or oil, body lotion, base coat, coloured polish, top coat.

Procedure

1) Remove all traces of existing polish.

2) Soak both feet in the bowl of soapy water for about five minutes (while you are doing this, you can use the time to remove old polish from your fingernails).

3) Use pumice stone on soles, heels and sides of feet to remove rough dry skin.

4) Dry feet carefully, particularly between the toes.

5) Apply cuticle cream or oil around the toenail and massage well. Then, using a rounded orange stick (reshape and soften the ends with a penknife and make sure there are no splinters to catch and tear your skin), gently push back the cuticles and help the

cream or oil to penetrate underneath and reach the matrix where the nails form and grow.

6) Rinse feet in warm clear water and dry again thoroughly.

7) Clip nails straight across; don't clip into the side or try to cut a curved shape as this encourages in-growing toenails, which are unsightly and painful. (Toenails shouldn't be too long or they will press against your shoes, but they should be all one length.)

8) File the ends smooth with an emery board. Massage toes and feet well with a moisturizing body lotion, then wipe the nail area clean with a tissue (polish won't stick if any greasiness is left.)

9) Twist tissue into two long sausage shapes and wind them in and out of your toes – this separates the toes and prevents polish smudging from one toe to the other.

10) Apply base coat – more important on toenails than fingernails as they tend to be rougher; this will provide a smooth foundation for polish.

11) Apply two coats of your chosen colour – and lastly a top coat if you wish. Allow each coat to dry between each application and let the final surface dry for at least half an hour when you've finished (about the time it takes to give yourself a manicure).

12) Lastly, massage well with body lotion again.

Manicure Repeat the process for pedicure, omitting the pumice stone and filing your nails into a gentle curve. Again, a shorter all-one-length shape is much prettier than varying lengths, so choose a medium length that you can maintain. Make-up or foundation for hands is not usually very satisfactory, except for photography, but there are fading creams to help minimize freckles or brown spots.

Just remember it is always better to wear no coloured polish at all than to go round with chipped or peeling finger- or toenails.

For a complete step-by-step description of a perfect manicure, see the companion volume, *Vogue Guide to Skin Care*.

Scent:
How to Make the Most of Its Fragrant Aura

The right fragrance, worn constantly, sprayed or smoothed on from head to foot, is a powerful beauty asset. It enhances glowing skin, perfect make-up, shining hair and is truly the final touch to beauty. It's more evocative than any other sense – just a passing whiff evokes a nostalgia for past loves and pleasures or brings a feeling of fear or distress with such speed you are amazed.

It is a *vital* element in beauty, but also one of the most personal and individual. What you like on yourself, what you like on some-one else and what others like on you *can* be one and the same scent but are much more likely to be three different fragrances. One of the most intriguing aspects is how scent reacts to skin – it smells of one thing in the bottle, another on immediate application, then as it warms up and involves the skin's chemistry, top, middle and base notes (as the various groups that form a blended perfume are called) begin to show their strength and the lasting, lingering fragrance that will be yours becomes apparent about half an hour later.

Body chemistry is as individual as fingerprints and however many costly ingredients go into one single fragrance, you, your skin, will add the final one. The oils, minerals and moisture secreted by glands below the skin's surface, plus the elements that form skin, are what will make one fragrance smell different on each member of a group of wearers.

What else changes fragrance? Smoking can reduce its lasting power, as can air pollution; internal or external medication can distort a scent; and where you apply it makes all the difference to its potency – the best places are pulse points where natural warmth will cause the scent to develop to its maximum level, but this needs some experimentation. Some women find the inside of the crook of the elbow is great; others find behind the knees, between the breasts, on the wrists, behind the ears or at the nape of the neck works best for them. All fragrance should be treated as an accessory – an essential one – that envelops you like the lightest silk shawl printed in a myriad of colours, trailing behind you as you walk . . .

All great perfumes are complex interweavings of scented strands – hundreds become part of one overall blend, each one playing an important role in the final effect. Some are light and cool, some heavy and warm; some bright and fresh, some dark and sensuous. Some act as stimulants, some as narcotics (and poppies aren't the only flowers to have this effect), some refresh, some lull. Some send out quiet, but insistent messages on a deep, primeval level . . . our sense of smell may be much less acute than other mammals', having been used less and less over the ages, but it is still keen enough to accept messages of attraction, disgust, reassurance or warning.

An expert 'nose', as the great perfume creators are called, can identify the main ingredients of a perfume but even with scientific help he will have trouble determining the exact quantities used in the final blend. And so the great scents retain their exclusivity. Many of these ingredients have been known and used since thousands of years before Christ – musk, sandalwood, camphor, myrrh and frankincense, for instance – and the word 'perfume' dates from the time when some ancient discovered, having walked through scented smoke, that the smell clung to his body and made him (or her) more attractive. Now there are synthetic equivalents for many of them and science has provided other interesting and long-lasting unidentifiable odours, but nothing really compares with the real thing, which is becoming rarer all the time, accounting for the soaring high costs of perfume and fragrant products.

Some women like to find one scent that suits them and stick to it for the rest of their lives, others like to change according to their mood and others find it a good idea to change according to the seasons (fresh, green fragrances for summer, warm, spicy ones for winter) or climate.

Whatever your preference, scent should become a part of your daily life. Don't think of it as something to wear only occasionally or as the last thing you add before leaving the house. Learn to layer it – splash on cologne or eau de toilette directly after a bath or shower (after drying yourself!) and use matching scented soaps, bath oil, powder and deodorant – then follow with the most concentrated version and use it sparingly. Your scent should be as personal as your signature. The right one could be as simple as the single scent of a herb or flower or it could be a complex mixture of flowers, roots, spice, wood, leaves, moss, fruit and animal notes (see below).

It's purely a matter of taste, yours and those around you, and to help you choose, here is **an A-Z of some of the terms used when describing scent and a few of the main ingredients involved** (cross-references, especially of common words used in a technical sense, are given in italic):

ABSOLUTE OR CONCRETE a pure concentrated oil distinguished from an *essential oil* by the process through which it is obtained.
ALDEHYDE a synthetic fragrance and vital ingredient in modern perfumery.
AMBERGRIS the spew of sperm whales goaded by indigestion and found floating on the ocean or cast up on beaches, mostly in the Indian Ocean or South Pacific. An unsurpassed *fixative* in perfume.
ANIMAL NOTES the natural *fixatives*: musk, civet, castoreum (from the beaver) and ambergris.

BERGAMOT an oil obtained from a small green orange found in Southern Italy. A synthetic version is widely used now as the natural oil was found to cause brown patches on skin exposed to strong sunlight.

BOUQUET a mixture of smells; also the smell developing (as with wine) as it warms.

CIVET a glandular secretion from the civet cat, found in North East Africa and used as a *fixative*.

CHYPRE a particular type of perfume; opinions differ as to its definition and origin. The base contains oakmoss, labdanum (cistus), calamus and styrax, but to this are added *animal, fruity* or *floral notes*, giving many variations to this heady appealing type.

CITRUS an essence from the citrus fruit family: orange (the flower and the fruit), lemon, grapefruit, neroli and bergamot; or a type of perfume with strong citrus notes: the fresh *green* varieties and most eau de colognes.

CLASSICS a term often applied to the famous named perfumes, mostly pre-1940, but also referring to more modern ones that have become very popular and earned a commanding position in the fragrance world.

COLOGNE a toilet water originating in the 18th century in the city of Cologne; now also a lighter version of a scent or perfume.

ENFLEURAGE the French method of extracting scent from flowers by forcing the flowers to yield their scent to purified cold fat; this is washed in alcohol and the alcohol distilled to extract the scent.

ESSENTIAL OILS the oils extracted by distillation.

FIXATIVE a substance that holds the more volatile ingredients, keeping them stable and harmonious. Can be either synthetic or the natural animal fixatives such as musk, civet, ambergris and castoreum.

FLORAL OR FLOWERY a scent smelling of flowers. Single florals evoke the scent of a single flower, although they may have a complicated blend of ingredients. Floral *bouquets*, or flowery scents, are a blend of several flowers, often combined with other ingredients, where the flowery notes are strongest. Often very sweet.

FRUITY a blend in which the sweet heavy smells of fruits like peach, quince, pineapple and passion-fruit are dominant.

GRASSE the ancient hill town in the South of France, renowned as the centre of the French perfume industry. This is where the *essential oils* and *absolutes* are coaxed from flowers, herbs, roots, spices, leaves and woods – some grown locally, many imported – then blended into famous and new perfumes.

GREEN a fresh, clean scent usually containing ingredients like pine, fern, moss, grass, flower stems and leaves, plus citrus.

HERBAL a scent in which the smell of rosemary, mint or lavender, for instance, is especially strong.

HYACINTH Madame de Pompadour's favourite perfume; so expensive that only the very rich could afford it. Now it is included in many *floral* or 'spring flower' blends.

INCENSE burning oil. A very ancient method of perfuming the atmosphere – modern versions include joss sticks, rings filled with oil to place on the light bulb and candles.

JASMINE a most valuable ingredient, second only to the rose, found in the majority of great scents and obtained from the white, intensely scented flower.

KYPHI the fabulous ancient Egyptian perfume, made famous by Cleopatra, probably made from herbs and resins like myrrh, spikenard and henna with fruits such as raisins.

LINGER the lasting quality or staying power provided by *fixatives* and possessed by most recently created scents.

MODERN a blend using primarily synthetic ingredients – floral, *green*, herbal, warm, *spicy* or unidentifiable.

MUSK a *fixative* derived from a glandular secretion of the musk deer found in Tibet and much prized for its erotic, lasting powers. It is said to have been worn by the Empress Joséphine and to have lingered in her rooms long after her death.

NOSE a master *parfumeur* whose sense of smell is so highly

83

developed and pure that he can not only recognize and 'break down' ingredients in existing scents but still create truly original new blends.

ORANGE FLOWER an ingredient from the sweet orange tree – a popular flower, found in many old and new scents, with an intoxicating smell, symbolic of youth and brides. Neroli, from the bitter orange tree, has a dryer fresher scent.

ORIENTAL a rich, warm variety of scent usually containing balsams, resins from aromatic Eastern woods and plants, musk, ambergris and the heavier flower scents – tuberose, gardenia, jasmine.

OTTO OR ATTAR a concentrated distilled essence, usually of the rose.

PATCHOULI an oil derived from the leaves of an East Indian plant with a dry, haunting odour not unlike pencil shavings. Often associated with cashmere shawls in the Victorian era.

ROOTS ingredients such as iris (or orris) root, which provides the scent of violets in many perfumes; also vetiver grass.

ROSE the flower most of whose many varieties – musk rose, tea rose, etc. – produce a sweet smell; most prized of all is the Bulgarian rose, without which few perfumes would exist today as they are. Precious and expensive – half a ton of petals must be crushed to make one pound of rose attar. The scent of roses was loved by Elizabeth I, whose ladies in waiting made rosewater wherever her court was assembled.

SANDALWOOD a scent from the wood of a parasitic tree that attaches itself to the roots of other trees – found mostly in India and Australia.

SPICE a variety of perfume heavier than *floral* but not as heavy as the *Oriental* types. Usually a blend of exotic flowers with spices like clove, ginger and cinnamon.

SYNTHETICS the fragrant inventions that emerge from laboratories – enormously useful in creating new perfumes and preventing prices from soaring even higher.

Top Note the smell you smell first, before the perfume has warmed on your skin and revealed the middle notes or remained on long enough to produce the base.

Tuberose a flower (no relation to the rose) which produces an intoxicating, distinctive fragrance.

Varieties the categories, also known as divisions or kinds, into which most scents are divided, e.g. *floral, green, Oriental, fruity, chypre.*

Vetiver a superb *essential oil* from the roots of an aromatic grass found in the islands of the Indian Ocean.

Violet both the flowers and leaves are valuable to perfumery but very difficult to extract. However, iris (or orris) root provides a similar smell. Violets were the favourite flower of the Empress Joséphine.

X that added quality that comes from your own chemistry and skin and warms to your personality.

Ylang Ylang the scent with a poignant bitter-sweet quality from the flower of the same name. It means 'flower of flowers' to the South Sea Islanders.

Zanzibar the place where spice markets abound and the air is redolent with the scent of cloves.

Do's and Don'ts

Don't mix scent with the sun. Some ingredients, when exposed to skin and sun, can cause allergies, rashes or brown patches. So, if you are spending time outside in hot sun, on the beach or water or skiing in the mountains, keep your fragrance for evening allure. Do store scent in a dark, cool place. Light can cause chemical reaction and change the nature of the fragrance. If it's well sealed and well stored, it will last about a year and still be true – unsealed, exposed to light and heat, it oxidizes and deteriorates quite fast. Don't try more than three scents at the same time when you're contemplating something new. This is about as many as the average nose can accept before becoming tired. Spray or dab a little on the inside of the wrist, do the same on the other wrist and try the back of one hand for the third. Wait a minute or so for each one to develop, then smell it before applying the next. And, don't make your final decision before smelling them all again half an hour later.

Do think of fragrance in a much wider context than just its original bottle. Investigate the possibilities of having eau de toilette (splash it on during the day and keep the more concentrated version for evening), bath oil, body lotion, talcum powder, soap, deodorant. And, look out for other accessories in the same fragrance – candles, coat-hangers, drawer sachets, room sprays, so that everything about you smells the same.

Don't try and transfer your favourite scent to a plastic bottle for travelling – it tends to evaporate through plastic and you may lose it all. Travel with a purse spray or a small sealed bottle that's not plastic.

Do try spraying your ironing board with fragrance before ironing shirts and dresses.

Don't waste your scent on the air instead of on you. Once a bottle has been opened, use it – it will only evaporate and lose its potency if you try to save it.

Tessa Traeger

Index

Acne 53
Aldehyde 81
Ambergris 81
Applicators 17, 28, 30
Astringents 13

Base *see* Make-up
Bergamot 82
Blackheads 53
Bleaching 30
Blemishes 16–17, 53
Blondes 47–8
Blusher 17, 19, 30, 49, 55
  cream 19
  powder 20, 38, 45
Bouquet 82
Brunettes 49
Brushes 23, 30–31
Buffer 31

Cake liner 23, 24
Calamine lotion 31
Camouflage 14, 16, 53, 54
Camphor 8, 80
Candlelight 38
Chypre 82
Circulation 13, 53
Citrus 82
Civet 82
Classics 82
Cleanser 34
Cologne 82
Colour(s)
  co-ordination 58–9
  for eyes 23
  and light 37–9
  for different skin colourings 47–51
Combs 23, 31
Concealer 14, 31
Cotton buds 31
Creams 16, 17, 42
  bleaching 30
  cuticle 31, 42, 76
  fading 32, 53

hand 33, 42

Dehydration 14, 42
Diet 13, 20
  for over-35s 53

Emery boards 31
Enfleurage 82
Essential oils 82
Eyelash(es)
  curlers 32
  dye 48
  false 48
Eye(s) 20, 62–5
  -brows 56, 70
  circles under 14
  cream 20
  liner 23
  make-up 32, 55
  make-up remover 20, 32
  shadow 19, 20, 45

Face 61–70
Fading cream 32–53
Feet 73, 76–7
Fingernails, false 32-3
Fixative 82
Foundation 14, 16, 33
  for black skin 50
  for blondes 48
  for dark skin 49
  for over-35s 54
Freckles 47–8
Freshener 13

Gels 16, 17, 47

Hair 45, 53
Hand(s) 27-8, 73-6
  cream 33, 42
Herbal 83
Highlighters 24, 28, 33, 61
  and black skin 50
  iridescent 38

89

Humidity 41–2
Hyacinth 83

Incense 83

Jasmine 83

Kohl 24, 33, 47, 50
Kyphi 83

Light 37
  electric 38
  neon 38
Lip(s) 25, 57, 68–70
  barrier 33
  brush 25
  colour 33
  gloss 25, 27
  -stick 25–7

Make-up
  base 14, 30
  for different colourings 47–51
  for over-35s 53–7
  remover 34
Manicure 28, 42, 73–5, 77
Mascara 24, 32, 34, 47
Melanin 48
Mirror 34
Moisturizer 13, 14, 37, 41–2, 47
Musk 83

Nails(s) 25, 28, 42, 73–5
  false 32–3
  pencil 34
  polish 28, 34, 75

Orange flower 84
Orange sticks 35
Oriental (skin type) 49
Oriental (variety of perfume) 84
Otto 84

Patchouli 84
Pedicure 73, 76–7
Pencil 17, 25, 34–5
  sharpener 35
Polish 34, 75
Pores 50, 53
Powder 17, 19, 35, 50, 54

blusher 20, 38, 45
  eye shadow 20
Psoriasis 53

Redheads 48
Rose 84
Rouge 17

Sandalwood 84
Scar 16
Scent 79–81
  terms 81–5
Skin
  black 50–51
  combination 13
  dark 49
  dry 13, 42, 47
  fair 47, 48
  freshener 13
  oily 13
  olive 49
  patchy 13, 53
  sensitive 13, 47
  toner 13
Soap-and-water 13, 41
Spice 84
Sponges 23, 35
Spots 16, 53
Sun 14
  -glasses 20, 41
  -screen 14, 37, 42, 45
  over-exposure to 41
Synthetics 84

Tan 19
Toner 13
Tuberose 85
Tweezers 35

Veins, broken 53
Vetiver 85
Violet 85

Weather, effect of 41–5
Whiteheads 53
Witch-hazel 42
Wrinkles 14

Ylang ylang 85

Zinc 35

ALSO BY FELICITY CLARK

VOGUE GUIDE TO SKIN CARE

Keep every inch of the skin of your body in glowing health! Here the Beauty Editor of *Vogue* shows you where your skin is most vulnerable, when to get expert advice; analyses facial types; describes proper cleansing, freshening and moisturizing and the changes that age brings; and discusses specialized problems. There is a whole section on total body care – diet, exercise, depilation, hands and feet, tanners and protectors – written to help you understand what causes and alleviates skin troubles, plus an A–Z of common skin problems.

VOGUE GUIDE TO HAIR CARE

The book for everyone who wants glossy, healthy hair! Here you can find out about your hair's structure and type, what happens to it with age, and how to look after it. The author advises you on finding a style to suit you and to keep you looking your best – whatever the weather. There is detailed advice on colouring with natural and man-made dyes, on permanent waving and straightening, and on styles for special occasions, wigs and hairpieces. And, as diet affects hair, the guide includes useful recipes, an A–Z of hair care, plus an illustrated glossary of recent cuts and styles.

Also in Penguin by Bronwen Meredith

VOGUE BODY AND BEAUTY BOOK

VOGUE NATURAL HEALTH AND BEAUTY

MORE ABOUT PENGUINS
AND PELICANS

For further information about books available from Penguins please write to Dept EP, Penguin Books Ltd, Harmondsworth, Middlesex UB7 ODA.

In the U.S.A.: For a complete list of books available from Penguins in the United States write to Dept CS, Penguin Books, 625 Madison Avenue, New York, New York 10022.

In Canada: For a complete list of books available from Penguins in Canada write to Penguin Books Canada Ltd, 2801 John Street, Markham, Ontario L3R 1B4.

In Australia: For a complete list of books available from Penguins in Australia write to the Marketing Department, Penguin Books Australia Ltd, P.O. Box 257, Ringwood, Victoria 3134.

In New Zealand: For a complete list of books available from Penguins in New Zealand write to the Marketing Department, Penguin Books (N.Z.) Ltd. P.O. Box 4019, Auckland 10.